DEDICATIONS

I would like to dedicate this book to all who are taking the journey toward emotional healing. You are incredible and I celebrate you.

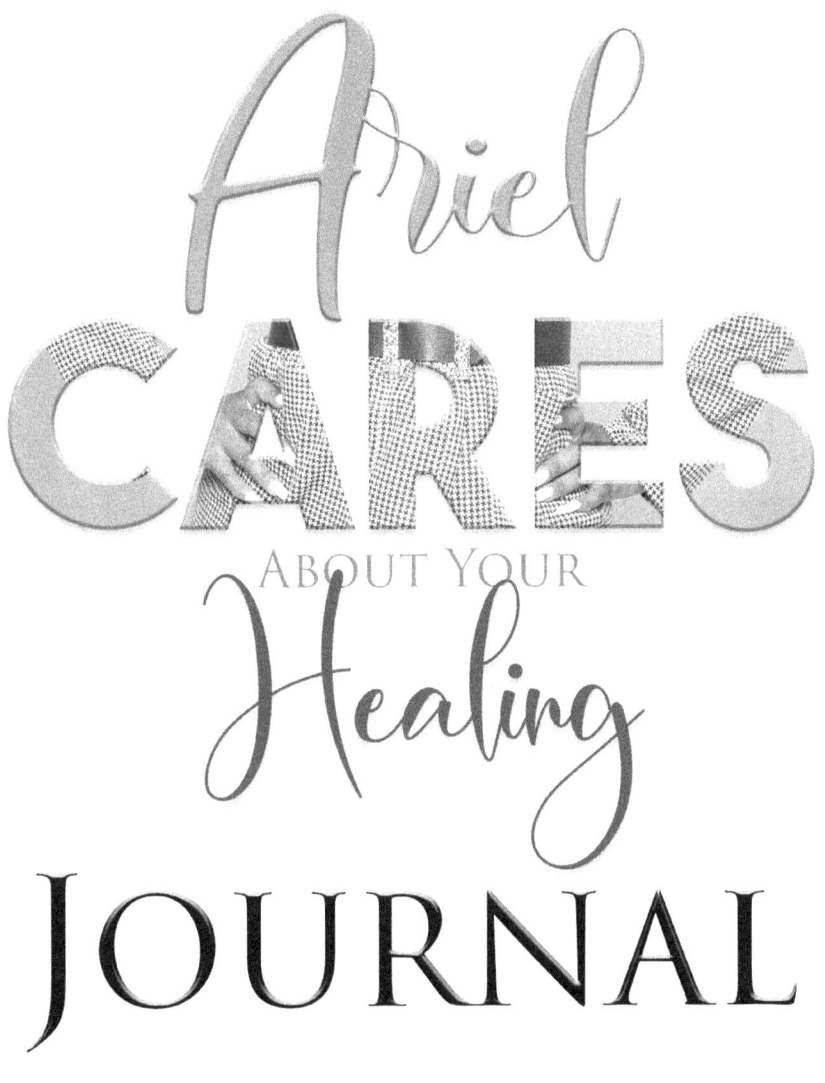

Ariel CARES About Your Healing Journal

Ariel Thomas

Ariel Cares About Your Healing Journal

Ariel Thomas

T&J Publishers

Printed in the United States of America by
T&J Publishers (Atlanta, GA.)
www.TandJPublishers.com

© Copyright 2021 by Ariel Thomas

All rights reserved. This book or parts thereof may not be reproduced in any form, stored in a retrieval system, or transmitted in any form by any means-electronic, mechanical, photocopy, recording, or otherwise-without prior written permission of the author, except as provided by United States of America copyright law.

All Bible verses are taken from the New International Version (NIV) and the New Living Translation (NLT).

Cover Design by Timothy Flemming, Jr.
(T&J Publishers)
Book Format/Layout by Timothy Flemming, Jr.

ISBN: 978-1-7376635-1-5

To contact the author, go to:
www.ArielCares.com
ArielCaresCoaching@gmail.com
Facebook: Ariel Thomas
Instagram: ariel_thecoach
Instagram: arielcares2018

RULES FOR THE JOURNEY

YOU ARE ON A JOURNEY TOWARDS emotional healing. In order to complete the journey, you must have a made up mind that you are going to go all the way. Be determined not to stop, no matter how hard it gets. Be willing to do all of the exercises no matter how simple or difficult they may seem. And don't just do the exercises; read over your work. Review what you've written. Recite what you've written out loud. That's the key to changing your heart and mind—declaring out loud the truth about yourself. Let your heart and mind hear your words.

Some of the exercises will tug on your heart and challenge you to face things about yourself you may not want to face. But that's the point. I want you to dig deep and confront the things you've been running from, the things that have you bound. Contrary to popular belief, it's what you don't see—or refuse to see—that's killing you. We're going to conquer these things together.

Grab your pen. It's time to get started.

ARIEL CARES ABOUT YOUR HEALING *JOURNAL*

1
Facing your Demons

Sometimes we must go backward before we can move forward. No, it's not always pleasant going back into the past and facing painful situations and circumstances, but it's necessary in order to gain the freedom that you need. You can't be free if you're unwilling to confront things you've been running from and avoiding. Fear will always rule and dominate your life. So I want you to do the exercise below.

Things you're going to need:

- A quiet spot where you can think and be alone
- A pen and piece of paper
- Some tissue (optional)

I want you to visit the past and think about the pivotal moments in your life where someone hurt you, made you feel low, criticized and ridiculed you, or abused you. It may take a little courage, but we're going to revisit every detail of what happened. This is not to reopen old wounds; it's to build the courage to face the past.

ARIEL CARES ABOUT YOUR HEALING *JOURNAL*

Sit and think. Cry if you have to. It's okay. Let the tears flow. Just know that the more exposure you give to the hidden things in your life, the more power you gain over these things.

Let's begin.

I remember when _____

_____

_____

_____

_____

_____

_____

_____

_____

_____

ARIEL CARES ABOUT YOUR HEALING *JOURNAL*

ARIEL CARES ABOUT YOUR HEALING *JOURNAL*

ARIEL CARES ABOUT YOUR HEALING *JOURNAL*

2
Identifying Your Inner Beliefs

For so many years, I held a negative view of myself because of the way I was raised. I called myself all kinds of negative things: loser, unlovable, rejected, the black sheep of the family, and more. I was rejected as a child by my mom, and this created within me the belief that I didn't matter. I was abused by my stepdad, and this created within me the belief that I deserved to be mistreated; that I wasn't worthy of respect. Behind every negative experience I had, I came up with a narrative to explain it. What messages did your negative experiences communicate to you about yourself? Write them down.

Remember: These messages are your internal beliefs about yourself.

Example:
Event: My mother rejected me.
The belief I received: "I am not good enough to receive love."
Event: My boyfriend cheated on me with my

best friend
The belief I received: "I am ugly and inferior to girls that look like my best friend."

Jot these internal beliefs down because we're going to change them in a moment.

_____

_____

_____

_____

_____

_____

_____

_____

_____

ARIEL CARES ABOUT YOUR HEALING *JOURNAL*

ARIEL CARES ABOUT YOUR HEALING *JOURNAL*

ARIEL CARES ABOUT YOUR HEALING *JOURNAL*

3
Changing Your Inner Beliefs

In our last exercise, I had you make a list of your internal beliefs. In this section, we're going to shift the focus from the negative messages about yourself and focus on the positives. I want you to do something you probably don't do enough of: think about every success and positive experience you've had and record what messages these experiences communicated to you.

We're going to do the same thing in this section that we did in the last section but in reverse.

Example:

Event: I overcame my fear of public speaking and gave a speech in front of a large audience.
The belief I received: "I can overcome any fear and accomplish any goal I set for myself."
Event: I purchased my first car with my own money
The belief I received: "I am strong and capable, and I can take care of myself. I don't need others to survive."

ARIEL CARES ABOUT YOUR HEALING *JOURNAL*

ARIEL CARES ABOUT YOUR HEALING *JOURNAL*

ARIEL CARES ABOUT YOUR HEALING *JOURNAL*

ARIEL CARES ABOUT YOUR HEALING *JOURNAL*

4
ELEVATION

THERE'S A SAYING THAT I HAVE: "ELEVATION requires separation." I stand by that philosophy. That philosophy is one of the things that saved my life. I had to learn that in order to reach higher heights in life, I needed to cut some people loose and leave some people behind. I had to cut negative people out of my life, people who spoke against my dreams and tried to discourage me. It didn't matter if they were family, friends, or associates. I had to guard and protect my ears.

Perhaps you have some dreams and goals you'd like to accomplish. If so, I want to encourage you to write them down. You need to know where you're going in order to better sort out who's equipped to walk with you along your journey. Once you record your dreams and goals, begin to think about the people who should be a part of your team. Realize that no one can accomplish great things in life without the right people around them.

_____

_____

ARIEL CARES ABOUT YOUR HEALING *JOURNAL*

ARIEL CARES ABOUT YOUR HEALING *JOURNAL*

ARIEL CARES ABOUT YOUR HEALING *JOURNAL*

ARIEL CARES ABOUT YOUR HEALING *JOURNAL*

5
THE POWER OF YOUR WORDS

I GAVE SEVERAL EXAMPLES IN THE BOOK OF the power of words. I didn't realize it at the time, but I was speaking life and success into other people while speaking defeat over myself. The funny thing is the other people I spoke over went on to experience incredible success. They opened businesses, acquired property, and more. On the other hand, it seemed like my life stayed in a rut. When I discovered this pattern, I decided to change the words I spoke over myself and I started speaking life and success over myself.

The Bible says the power of life and death is in the tongue. Are you using your tongue to plant the seeds of blessings in your life, or are you using your tongue to sow seeds of curses in your life?

Today's assignment is to practice being conscious of your words as you go throughout your day. Practice speaking life, speaking positively over every situation you encounter. Catch every word before it proceeds from your mouth and make sure you examine it before you let it slip from your tongue. Today, no negative words.

ARIEL CARES ABOUT YOUR HEALING *JOURNAL*

ARIEL CARES ABOUT YOUR HEALING *JOURNAL*

ARIEL CARES ABOUT YOUR HEALING *JOURNAL*

ARIEL CARES ABOUT YOUR HEALING *JOURNAL*

6
Discovering You Again

ONE OF THE MOST IMPORTANT DISCOVERIES you can make is self-discovery. It's important that you take time out of your life to discover yourself: what makes you tick, what you like and dislike, what your preferences are, what you enjoy doing. So many people have never taken the time to get to know themselves, and it's because of this they spiral into frustration while trying to be what everyone else wants them to be. If other people's preferences, wants, and needs are so important to you, then what about yours? Aren't your wants, needs, and desires just as important and deserving of attention? Sure they are. You just need to identify them. So in this section, I want you to write down your deepest wants and needs, and your preferences in life. If it takes you a minute to figure these things out, take all of the time you need. It's about time you devote some time to thinking about what makes you you.

ARIEL CARES ABOUT YOUR HEALING *JOURNAL*

ARIEL CARES ABOUT YOUR HEALING *JOURNAL*

ARIEL CARES ABOUT YOUR HEALING *JOURNAL*

ARIEL CARES ABOUT YOUR HEALING *JOURNAL*

7
Affirmations

MY LIFE BEGAN TO CHANGE WHEN I discovered the power and importance of speaking affirmations over myself. First, I had to learn that it wasn't someone else's job to affirm me; and second, I had to learn how to affirm myself even when I didn't feel like it. It's normal to want to sit and stew in your self-pity and feel miserable, but picking yourself up is your job in life. You can't sit back and complain about other people not picking you up and carrying you on their backs—they're weighed down enough with their own burdens and don't have room to carry yours. You have the strength and the power to speak over yourself, as we established already. But now, I want you to be very specific in creating a set of affirmations you're going to declare over yourself each day. As you speak these affirmations, you will begin to feel your attitude towards yourself changing.

In the beginning, you might feel weird speaking these affirmations over yourself, especially if you've never done this before. However, as time progresses, you will begin to feel a difference within yourself, and speaking these affirmations will become a normal part of your daily routine, as normal as breathing.

ARIEL CARES ABOUT YOUR HEALING *JOURNAL*

Below, I've compiled a list of affirmations I created for myself. You can use these affirmations, or you can create your own list. Either way, it's time to get started affirming who you are.

- "I am beautiful."
- "I am strong."
- "I am courageous."
- "I am confident in who God made me."
- "I succeed in everything I do."
- "I am a queen."
- "I love myself."
- "I am good enough all by myself."
- "I love life."
- "I was designed for greatness in this world."
- "People love me because I enrich their lives and bring out the best in them."
- "I am free from other people's opinions and expectations of me."
- "I am not a failure. Even when things don't go as planned, I always pick myself and try again. I always accomplish my goals no matter how long it takes."
- "I have purpose. I exist for a reason."

_____

_____

ARIEL CARES ABOUT YOUR HEALING *JOURNAL*

ARIEL CARES ABOUT YOUR HEALING *JOURNAL*

ARIEL CARES ABOUT YOUR HEALING *JOURNAL*

8
Redefining Who You Are

*I*F I HAD TO LIVE MY LIFE BASED ON THE LABELS other people placed on me, including mental health experts, teachers, and more, then I'd be a basket case whose life is doomed to failure. I would either be dead or in prison. Thank God, I didn't accept the labels placed on me by others, but I instead sought to discover what God said about me.

In the last section, we practiced creating and speaking affirmations over ourselves. In this section, we're going to practice casting off labels that have been placed on us by others and putting on the right labels. Now, this section is designed to jumpstart you into reading God's Word. Why? Because God is the one who created you and He's the only one that has the right to label you. How? I'm going to do this by having you investigate God's Word, the Bible, for revelations about who God says you are and what He thinks about you. Yes, I'm going to have you look up Bible verses that talk about your identity and that reveal what God's thoughts are concerning you. Use the internet. Use a Bible commentary. Talk to a preacher or

Bible teacher. It doesn't matter. I just want you to read the verses from the Bible yourself and then jot them down in this section.

After you find these verses, I want you to write down your thoughts about each verse. I want you to explain in detail what each verse means to you—what message they communicate to you and how these messages affect the way that you feel about yourself. To give you a head-start, I've listed a few Bible verses for you:

Psalm 139:13–14
"For you created my inmost being; you knit me together in my mother's womb. I praise you because I am fearfully and wonderfully made; your works are wonderful, I know that full well."

Genesis 1:27
"So God created man in his own image, in the image of God he created him; male and female he created them."

2 Corinthians 5:17
"Therefore, if anyone is in Christ, he is a new creation. The old has passed away; behold, the new has come."

Jeremiah 29:11
"For I know the plans I have for you," declares the LORD, "plans to prosper you and not to harm you, plans to give you hope and a future."

Now, it's time for you to discover and record what God says about you in His Word.

ARIEL CARES ABOUT YOUR HEALING *JOURNAL*

ARIEL CARES ABOUT YOUR HEALING *JOURNAL*

ARIEL CARES ABOUT YOUR HEALING *JOURNAL*

ARIEL CARES ABOUT YOUR HEALING *JOURNAL*

9

Forgiveness

*I*T MAY SEEM DIFFICULT TO FORGIVE THOSE who hurt you, but it's necessary. This is perhaps the most important step in the mental and emotional healing process. So many people walk around carrying the heavyweight of unforgiveness. They're weighed down and don't know it. They're sitting around waiting and expecting people to come to them and apologize for the way they acted. If you're in that boat, then you may find yourself waiting for a lifetime. Some people may never apologize to you for the way they treated you, for the things they did and said concerning you. But you shouldn't put your life on pause just for them. God promised to take care of those who did you wrong, but He also told us that the key to both receiving forgiveness from Him and living a life of true freedom is in forgiving others.

    Forgiveness isn't about the other person; it isn't about "letting them off the hook"; it's about freeing yourself from the emotional baggage that weighing you down. When you forgive, you let go of the heavyweight of expectation—you stop waiting and expecting other people to release you—and you free yourself. You choose to place them in God's hands and move forward with your life. Are

ARIEL CARES ABOUT YOUR HEALING *JOURNAL*

there any people you need to forgive today? I'm sure there are. There are always people we need to forgive. Why? Because it's human to make mistakes and walk in error. Think about the many people you've done wrong. We're only human. So forgive today. Forgive others, and forgive yourself. Grow from your mistakes rather than wallowing in them like a pig. Remember: What doesn't kill you only makes you stronger.

_____

_____

_____

_____

_____

_____

_____

_____

ARIEL CARES ABOUT YOUR HEALING *JOURNAL*

ARIEL CARES ABOUT YOUR HEALING *JOURNAL*

ARIEL CARES ABOUT YOUR HEALING *JOURNAL*

Prayer

Dear Heavenly Father, I thank you that you are a healer and a deliverer. I thank you that you created me with a purpose in mind. I exist for a reason. Thank you for your grace and mercy in my life, and for protecting me throughout the years. Even though it didn't look like it at times, you were always there with me through everything I faced. It may have felt like it at times, but I was never alone. And you promised to never leave nor forsake me.

Father, I surrender my life to you. I accept the Lord Jesus into my heart and allow you to lead and guide my life. I know that you are doing wonderful work in my heart. You are healing my heart today. You are healing every open wound in my soul. I thank you for healing from every rejection. I thank you by faith that you have set me free from the pain of the past, and that by faith I am also free from every generational curse placed on my family. It is through the blood of Jesus that I have obtained freedom from every curse and fear and that I am a brand new person with a bright future.

Father, I place into your hands every person that has ever hurt me. I give them to you today and pray that you will heal their hearts and bring correction and humility into their lives. I pray for them. I pray that you will remove the blinders from their eyes and give them a revelation of your love and purpose for their lives.

Father, I forgive those who hurt me. I release any and all malice, anger, and bitterness I have in my heart towards them. I understand that they were operating in ignorance. They were only doing what they were taught.

Today, I declare and decree that I am free and that I am blessed and highly favored. I am predestined to live a successful life. Fill my heart with your love and teach me your ways. Lead me, guide me, speak to me concerning your will for my life, and reveal to me your purpose for my life. I surrender to you today. This, I pray, in Jesus name, amen.

Additional Notes

ARIEL CARES ABOUT YOUR HEALING *JOURNAL*

ARIEL CARES ABOUT YOUR HEALING *JOURNAL*

ARIEL CARES ABOUT YOUR HEALING *JOURNAL*

ARIEL CARES ABOUT YOUR HEALING *JOURNAL*

The journey begins with the book
"ARIEL CARES ABOUT YOUR HEALING"

Pick up your copy of Ariel Thomas' debut book and discover the keys to overcoming emotional trauma, abuse, rejection and abandonment and gain the power to transform your life.

Available wherever books are sold: Amazon, Barnes & Noble, etc.

www.ingramcontent.com/pod-product-compliance
Lightning Source LLC
Chambersburg PA
CBHW071834290426
44109CB00017B/1822